Collins

04/0

MATHS FRAMEWORKING

Complete success for Mathematics at KS3

YEAR 7 **WORKBOOK**

Contents

Exercise 1A Words and numbers

This exercise will give you practice in

- reading and writing numbers in figures and words

1 Write these words in number form.

a twenty-seven _____

b thirty-four _____

c one hundred and fifty-two _____

d three hundred and sixty-four _____

e seven hundred and forty-one _____

f one thousand one hundred and one _____

g two thousand four hundred and forty _____

h nine thousand five hundred and twenty-one _____

2 Write these numbers in word form.

a 35 _____

b 56 _____

c 179 _____

d 284 _____

e 997 _____

f 1678 _____

_____

g 1002 _____

_____

h 1999 _____

_____

3 Kamal is a second-hand car salesman. He wants to put the price of each car on its windscreen in numbers. Write in the price of each car on its windscreen.

a   two thousand five hundred pounds

b   one thousand one hundred and ninety-nine pounds

c   nine hundred and ninety-nine pounds

d   five hundred pounds

e   two thousand and ninety-nine pounds

4 Which is the cheapest car in **Question 3**? _____

Exercise 1B   Addition

> **This exercise will give you practice in**
> - adding together two whole numbers

1 Use any method to work out each of the following additions.

a 34 + 57	**b** 72 + 78	**c** 66 + 23
d 92 + 34	**e** 46 + 59	**f** 91 + 23

g 32 + 77   **h** 65 + 56   **i** 94 + 67

2 Use any method to work out each of the following additions.

a 174 + 75   **b** 362 + 62   **c** 473 + 66

d 286 + 345   **e** 765 + 434   **f** 676 + 545

g 975 + 323   **h** 778 + 334   **i** 265 + 799

3 Choose one number from Box A and one number from Box B to make five addition calculations. Work out the answer to each of your calculations in the box below.

Box A			
165	757	334	28
742	654	224	

Box B			
72	659	99	286
462	889	999	

Exercise 1C   Subtraction

This exercise will give you practice in
- subtracting two whole numbers

1 Use any method to work out each of the following subtractions.

a 74 – 34	**b** 78 – 72	**c** 66 – 23
d 92 – 34	**e** 46 – 39	**f** 91 – 23
g 98 – 77	**h** 65 – 56	**i** 94 – 67

2 Use any method to work out each of the following subtractions.

a 286 – 145	**b** 765 – 434	**c** 778 – 334
d 174 – 77	**e** 362 – 64	**f** 634 – 545
g 975 – 386	**h** 473 – 66	**i** 265 – 199

3 Choose one number from Box A and one number from Box B to make five subtraction calculations. Work out the answer to each of your calculations in the box below.

Remember, your first number needs to be bigger than your second number.

A
165   757   334   28
742   654   224

B
72   659   99   286
462   889   999

Exercise 1D Using a calculator

This exercise will give you practice in

- using a calculator for addition, subtraction, multiplication and division

1 Use a calculator to work out these calculations. Write your answers in the spaces provided. Remember to enter the numbers carefully and check the operation!

a 4823 + 767 _____

b 6752 + 3467 _____

c 3923 + 567 _____

d 7465 + 986 _____

e 2232 + 4466 _____

f 7654 − 3345 _____

g 8345 − 641 _____

h 4588 − 323 _____

i 8822 − 222 _____

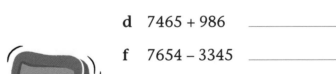

j 4294 − 4291 _____

k 72 × 44 _____

l 78 × 22 _____

m 99 × 100 _____

n 156 × 223 _____

o 5724 ÷ 36 _____

p 14 736 ÷ 48 _____

q 79 856 ÷ 1426 _____

r 91 416 ÷ 52 _____

2 **a** 2 3 5 4

Use any of the numbers and the + key on your calculator to make 10.
Write down your calculation.

_____

b 2 6 7 4

Use any of the numbers and the + key on your calculator to make 17.
Write down your calculation.

_____

c 5 2 4 8

Use any of the numbers and the + key on your calculator to make 14.
Write down your calculation.

_____

d 7 4 9 8 1 2

Use any of the numbers and the + key on your calculator to make 20.
Write down your calculation.

_____

e 14 11 5 8 3

Use any of the numbers and the − key on your calculator to make 1.
Write down your calculation.

_____

f 17 3 7 4 2

Use any of the numbers and the − key on your calculator to make 6.
Write down your calculation.

_____

Exercise 1E   Negative numbers

This exercise will give you practice in
- ordering a set of positive and negative integers
- calculating a temperature rise and fall across 0

1 Put each set of numbers in order from smallest to largest.

a 2, 7, −2, 3, 5, −3, 0 _____

b –7, 4, –5, 6, 1, –1, 2 _____

c 9, 6, –5, 4, –3, –4, 2, 7, –2, 0 _____

d 6, 4, –2, –3, 9, 7, –4, 6, 0, –1 _____

2 Look at the thermometers and answer the questions.

a

If the temperature increases by 3°C what will the temperature be? _____

b

If the temperature falls by 5°C what will the temperature be? _____

c

If the temperature falls by 4°C what will the temperature be? _____

d

If the temperature increases by 6°C what will the temperature be? _____

e

If the temperature increases by 2°C what will the temperature be? _____

f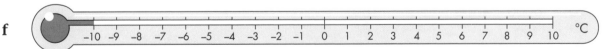

If the temperature increased by 15°C what will the temperature be? _____

g

If the temperature decreases by 20°C what will the temperature be? _____

h

If the temperature increases by 12°C what will the temperature be? _____

Exercise 1F Multiplying by 10 and 100

This exercise will give you practice in
multiplying positive integers by 10 or 100
recognising the place value of numbers

1 Number bingo

Play this game with the person next to you.

a Take it in turns to choose one of the operations and one of the numbers from the line below.

| ×10 | ×100 | | 500 | 45 | 95 | 30 | 400 | 350 | 16 | 60 | 7 | 10 | 12 | 8 | 200 | 9 |

b Multiply them to make one of the numbers in the grid below.

c If you were right, cross the number out on the grid.

d The winner is the person that crosses out five numbers in a line in any direction.

1600	450	400	100	120
3500	900	2000	70	1600
300	600	1200	700	3500
5000	3000	80	800	950
90	6000	4500	9500	160

2 Complete the multiplication grids.

a

×	10	100
55		
650		
31		
433		

b

×	10	100
6		
24		
72		
67		

c

×	10	100
333		
47		
82		
77		

3 Look at these numbers. In each number one digit is red. Write down what this digit represents.

a   405 395 _____

b   123 307 _____

c   165 788 _____

d   350 211 _____

e   896 473 _____

f   157 699 _____

g   352 147 _____

h   452 361 _____

Exercise 2A Number sequences

This exercise will give you practice in
- recognising and extending number sequences

1 **a** Add 10 each time to get to the top of the stairs.

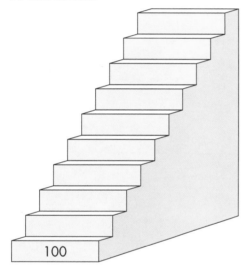

b Add 20 each time to get to the top of the stairs.

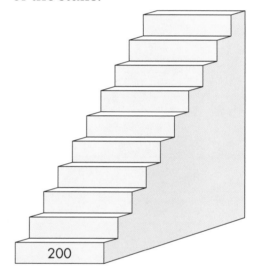

c Add 25 each time to get to the top of the stairs.

d Subtract 10 each time to get to the bottom of the stairs.

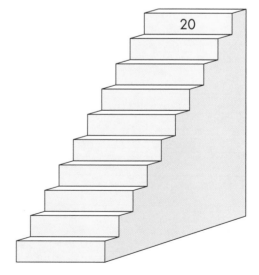

e   Subtract 20 each time to get to the bottom of the stairs.

f   Subtract 25 each time to get to the bottom of the stairs.

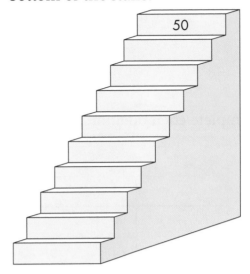

2 a   Write down all the multiples of 6 in order from –60 to 60.

b   Write down all the multiples of 8 in order from –80 to 80.

c   Which multiples appear in both lists **a** and **b**?

3 Using your two lists of multiples from **Question 2**, complete the table below.

Start	Add/subtract	Finish
8	+ one lot of 8	
16	+ three lots of 8	
12	+ two lots of 6	
–6	– three lots of 6	
–24	+ four lots of 8	
–64	+ three lots of 8	
56	– four lots of 8	
36	– six lots of 6	

Exercise 2B Odd and even numbers

This exercise will give you practice in

- recognising odd and even numbers and their properties

1 Complete each addition in the following tables.

+	Even			
	4	6	2	8
6 (Even)	10			
2				
8				
4				
10				

+	Odd			
	7	11	3	13
1 (Odd)				
5				
9				
3				
7				

+	Odd			
	7	3	9	11
6 (Even)				
2				
8				
4				
10				

2 Use the numbers opposite to help you complete the following sentences by crossing out the wrong answer. You should try at least four examples for each sentence on rough paper before deciding on the answer.

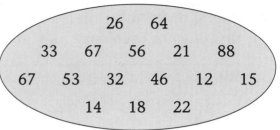

26 64

33 67 56 21 88

67 53 32 46 12 15

14 18 22

a The sum of two even numbers is always ODD/EVEN.

b The sum of two odd numbers is always ODD/EVEN.

c The sum of an odd number and an even number is always ODD/EVEN.

d The difference between two odd numbers is always ODD/EVEN.

e The difference between two even numbers is always ODD/EVEN.

f The difference between an odd number and an even number is always ODD/EVEN.

Exercise 2C   Rounding

This exercise will give you practice in

- rounding any positive integer less than 1000 to the nearest 10 or 100

1 Round each of these numbers to the nearest multiple of 10.

a 64 _____ **b** 72 _____ **c** 89 _____

d 23 _____ **e** 65 _____ **f** 14 _____

g 26 _____ **h** 31 _____ **i** 25 _____

j 77 _____ **k** 66 _____ **l** 34 _____

2 Round each of these numbers to the nearest multiple of 100.

a 734 _____ **b** 576 _____ **c** 212 _____

d 788 _____ **e** 899 _____ **f** 150 _____

g 129 _____ **h** 233 _____ **i** 643 _____

j 349 _____ **k** 743 _____ **l** 379 _____

3 Round the numbers in the table to the nearest multiple of 10 and 100. The first one has been done for you.

Number	Nearest multiple of 10	Nearest multiple of 100
341	340	300
136		
765		
551		
899		
224		
665		
421		
199		
201		
862		
752		
334		
991		

Exercise 2D   Square numbers

This exercise will give you practice in
- using and learning squares of numbers to at least 10×10

1 Write a multiplication fact and a square number fact for each picture using the example below as a guide.

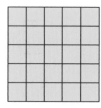

$5 \times 5 = 25$
$5^2 = 25$

a

_____

_____

b

_____

_____

c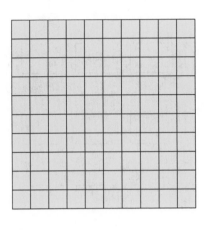

_____

_____

d

_____

_____

f

_____

_____

e

_____

_____

g

_____

_____

2 Complete each of the following.

a ____^{2} = 36 **b** 10×10 = ____ **c** ____^{2} = 81 **d** $8 \times$ ____ = 64

e ____^{2} = 16 **f** ____ $\times$ ____ = 49 **g** 6×6 = ____ **h** ____^{2} = 4

i 7^2 = ____ **j** ____ $\times$ ____ = 1 **k** ____^{2} = 100 **l** 9×9 = ____

m ____^{2} = 25

Exercise 2E   Sequences

This exercise will give you practice in

- generating and describing simple integer sequences

1 Write the next 10 numbers in each of these number sequences using the rule shown.

a   The rule is add on 2 each time.

22, 24, 26, ☐, ☐, ☐, ☐, ☐, ☐, ☐, ☐, ☐, ☐

b   The rule is add on 3 each time.

36, 39, 42, ☐, ☐, ☐, ☐, ☐, ☐, ☐, ☐, ☐, ☐

c   The rule is add on 4 each time.

12, 16, 20, ☐, ☐, ☐, ☐, ☐, ☐, ☐, ☐, ☐, ☐

d   The rule is subtract on 3 each time.

72, 69, 66, ☐, ☐, ☐, ☐, ☐, ☐, ☐, ☐, ☐, ☐

e   The rule is subtract on 10 each time.

320, 310, 300, ☐, ☐, ☐, ☐, ☐, ☐, ☐, ☐, ☐, ☐

f   The rule is double the number each time.

5, 10, 20, ☐, ☐, ☐, ☐, ☐, ☐, ☐, ☐, ☐, ☐

2 Write the next 5 numbers in each of these number sequences and then write the rule.

a   3, 8, 13, ☐, ☐, ☐, ☐, ☐

The rule is _____

b   2, 4, 8, 16, ☐, ☐, ☐, ☐, ☐

The rule is _____

c   98, 92, 86, ☐, ☐, ☐, ☐, ☐

The rule is _____

d   55, 66, 77, ☐, ☐, ☐, ☐, ☐

The rule is _____

Exercise 3A   Length and perimeter

This exercise will give you practice in

- drawing straight lines accurately
- converting measurements between millimetres and centimetres and vice versa
- calculating the perimeter of a rectangle by adding the lengths of its sides
- calculating the perimeter of a rectangle using the formula
  perimeter = 2 lengths + 2 widths

1 Draw accurately in the space below lines of the following lengths. Label your lines.

  a 3 cm   **b** 4 cm   **c** 20 mm   **d** 40 mm

2 Convert the following measurements into centimetres, using fractions when needed.

  a 45 mm   **b** 30 mm   **c** 27 mm   **d** 68 mm

3 Convert the following measurements into millimetres.

  a 6 cm   **b** 12 cm   **c** 3 cm   **d** $4\frac{1}{2}$ cm

4 Calculate the perimeter of each of the following rectangles.

a
2 cm
1 cm   1 cm
2 cm

b
3 cm
1 cm   1 cm
3 cm

c
5 cm
2 cm   2 cm
5 cm

_____

_____

5 Calculate the perimeter of the following rectangles using the formula
perimeter = 2 lengths + 2 widths. Show your working.

a
3 cm
2 cm

b
4 cm
1 cm

c
5 cm
3 cm

_____

_____

_____

6 Carole wants to put a fence around her vegetable garden. She draws a sketch of the garden to help her.

How much fencing will she need? Show your working.

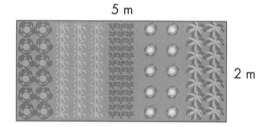

5 m

2 m

_____

_____

_____

Exercise 3B   Area

This exercise will give you practice in

- calculating the area of rectangles and other simple shapes using a counting method
- calculating the area of a rectangle or square using the formula **area = length × breadth**

1 **a** Find the area of the rectangle in cm² if the rectangle is made of up squares that measure 1 cm × 1 cm.

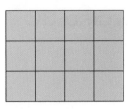

_____

b Find the area of the patio in m² if all of the patio slabs measure 1 m × 1 m.

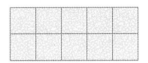

_____

2 David and Moira are buying new tiles for their kitchen floor. The floor is an 'L' shape. How many 1 m² floor tiles will they need to cover the whole area of the kitchen floor?

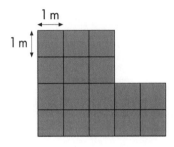

_____

_____

3 Find the area of each of the following shapes using the formula **area = length × breadth**. Show your working.

a   2 cm

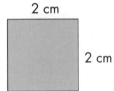

2 cm

b   3 m

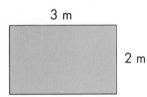

2 m

c   4 cm

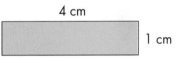

1 cm

_____   _____   _____

d   5 m

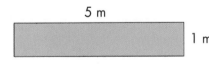

1 m

e   4 m

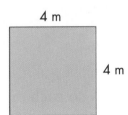

4 m

f   8 cm

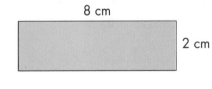

2 cm

_____   _____   _____

4 Which of the shapes in **Question 3** have the same area?

_____

Exercise 3C   3-D Shapes and nets

This exercise will give you practice in
- learning the names of some regular 3-D shapes
- recognising which type of net makes an open cube
- recognising how many faces, vertices and edges that regular 3-D shapes have

1 Fill in the blanks to name the following regular 3-D shapes:

a   **b**   **c**    **d**

c_b ___   c_b_i ___   square-based py__a__i __   t_t_a_ed_____

2 Circle the net you think will make an open cube. The base has been shaded to help you.

a   **b** 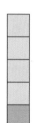   **c**   **d**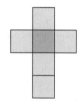

3 A cuboid has six faces, eight vertices and twelve edges.

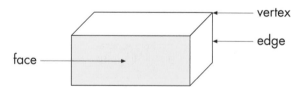

face   edge   vertex

How many faces, vertices and edges do each of these 3-D shapes have?

a

Faces _____

Vertices _____

Edges _____

b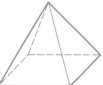

Faces _____

Vertices _____

Edges _____

c

Faces _____

Vertices _____

Edges _____

Exercise 3D   Perimeters of regular polygons

This exercise will give you practice in

- calculating the perimeter of a regular polygon by measuring its sides
- calculating the perimeter of a regular polygon by using the formula

  perimeter = length of side × number of sides

1 Calculate the perimeter of each of the following regular polygons by using a ruler to measure each side.

a    **b** 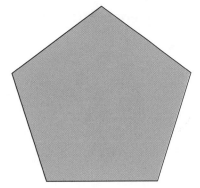   **c**

_____   _____   _____

2 Work out the perimeter of each of these regular polygons using the formula **perimeter = length of side × number of sides**.

a 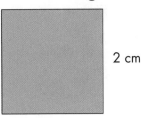   **b** 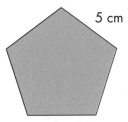 5 cm   **c** 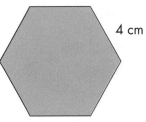 4 cm

2 cm

_____   _____   _____

_____   _____   _____

3 a Calculate the perimeter of the regular pentagon shown.

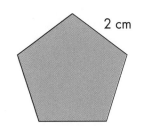 2 cm

_____

b What would the perimeter be if each side were

   i 3 cm _____

   ii 4 cm _____

   iii 6 cm _____

Exercise 4A   Improper fractions and mixed numbers

This exercise will give you practice in
- using fractions
- converting improper fractions into mixed numbers

1 What fraction of pizza is left? Write each fraction in numbers and words.

a
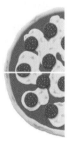

_____

_____

b
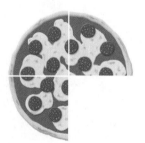

_____

_____

c

_____

_____

d

_____

_____

e

_____

_____

f

_____

_____

c
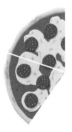

_____

_____

d

_____

_____

e

_____

_____

2 Look at the cakes. Describe the pieces left in two ways, as a mixed number and as an improper fraction. The first one has been done for you.

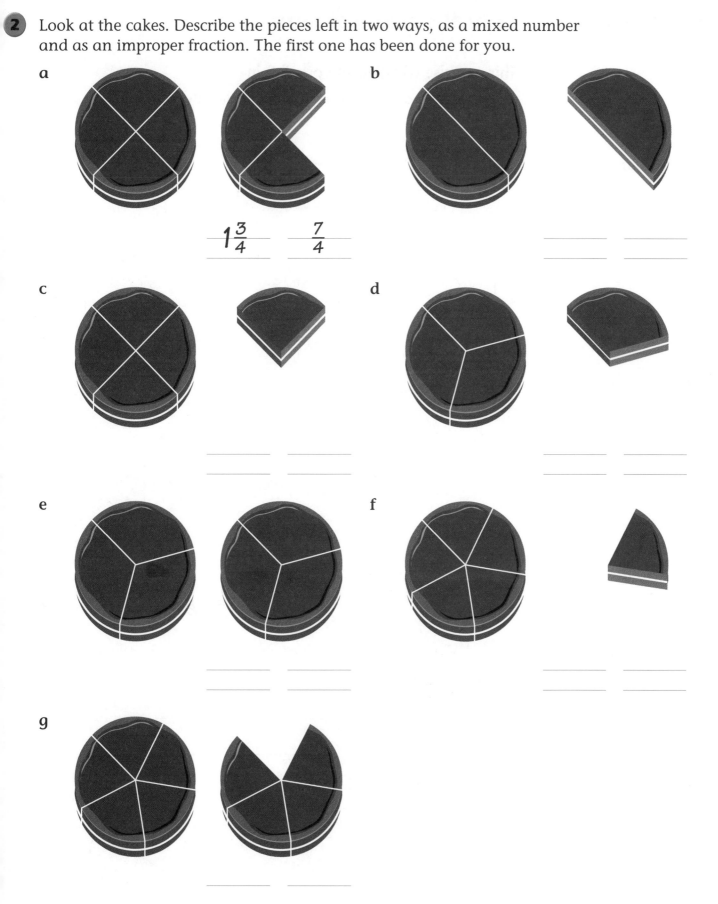

a

$\dfrac{1\frac{3}{4}}{\rule{3em}{0.4pt}}$ $\dfrac{\frac{7}{4}}{\rule{3em}{0.4pt}}$

b

c

d

e

f

g

Exercise 4B Equivalent fractions

This exercise will give you practice in
- recognising and finding equivalent fractions

1 Colour in the amounts that make a half.

a   b   c   d   e

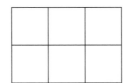  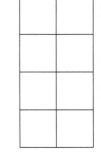

2 Colour in the amounts that make a quarter.

a   b   c

3 Find the equivalent fractions. One has been done for you.

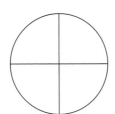 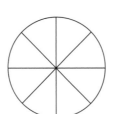

$\dfrac{1}{2}$ $\dfrac{2}{4}$ $\dfrac{3}{4}$ $\dfrac{6}{8}$ $\dfrac{9}{12}$ $\dfrac{5}{10}$

$\dfrac{6}{9}$ $\dfrac{2}{3}$ $\dfrac{4}{8}$ $\dfrac{3}{9}$ $\dfrac{1}{3}$ $\dfrac{2}{6}$

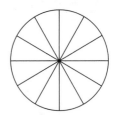

$$\dfrac{1}{2} = \dfrac{4}{8}$$

_____

_____

_____

_____

4 Colour in the equivalent fractions for a third.

 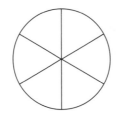 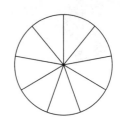

5 Colour in the equivalent fractions for a fifth.

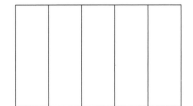 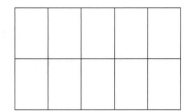 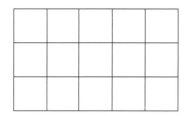

Exercise 4C Ordering fractions

This exercise will give you practice in
- finding equivalent fractions
- ordering a set of fractions with different numerators and denominators on a number line

1 Write down the fractions that are equivalent to $\frac{1}{2}$.

_____

_____

_____

$$\frac{2}{3} \quad \frac{2}{4} \quad \frac{4}{8} \quad \frac{5}{10} \quad \frac{3}{6} \quad \frac{2}{5} \quad \frac{1}{4} \quad \frac{2}{8} \quad \frac{3}{8}$$

2 Fill in the missing number in each of these equivalent fractions.

a $\frac{1}{3} = \frac{}{15}$ b $\frac{1}{4} = \frac{}{12}$ c $\frac{1}{2} = \frac{}{8}$ d $\frac{2}{5} = \frac{}{15}$ e $\frac{2}{3} = \frac{}{9}$

3 Look at the number line below.

0 —————————————————————————— 1

a Write in $\frac{1}{2}$ on the number line.   b Write in $\frac{1}{3}$ on the number line.
c Write in $\frac{1}{4}$ on the number line.   d Write in $\frac{1}{5}$ on the number line.

4 Look at the number line below.

0 —————————————————————————— 1

a Write in $\frac{3}{4}$ on the number line.   b Write in $\frac{2}{3}$ on the number line.
c Write in $\frac{3}{5}$ on the number line.   d Write in $\frac{7}{10}$ on the number line.

Exercise 4D   Fractions of quantities and numbers

This exercise will give you practice in
- finding fractions of numbers and quantities.

1 Find half of each of the following quantities.

a	100 cm	_____	**b**	80 g	_____	**c**	200 km	_____
d	120 m	_____	**e**	740 cm	_____	**f**	820 mm	_____
g	1400 m	_____	**h**	340 g	_____	**i**	62 m	_____
j	256 cm	_____	**k**	178 km	_____	**l**	920 mm	_____

2 Find a quarter of each of the following quantities.

a	100 m	_____	**b**	16 km	_____	**c**	240 cm	_____
d	120 l	_____	**e**	600 mm	_____	**f**	360 g	_____
g	1000 km	_____	**h**	880 m	_____	**i**	1600 km	_____
j	256 cm	_____	**k**	1200 mm	_____	**l**	3200 m	_____

3 Find a third of each of the following quantities.

a	90 m	_____	**b**	120 cm	_____	**c**	240 km	_____
d	36 m	_____	**e**	300 g	_____	**f**	360 kg	_____
g	900 m	_____	**h**	1800 m	_____	**i**	990 g	_____
j	330 km	_____	**k**	9000 mm	_____	**l**	1500 m	_____

4 How many sixths are there in each of the following whole numbers?

   a 6 _____   **b** 18 _____   **c** 36 _____   **d** 48 _____

5 How many eighths are there in each of the following whole numbers?

   a 8 _____   **b** 56 _____   **c** 80 _____   **d** 800 _____

Exercise 4E   Decimal fractions

This exercise will give you practice in
- using decimal notation for tenths
- ordering decimal fractions with one decimal place

1 Write the tenths from 0 to 1 as decimal fractions.

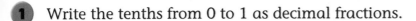

0   0.1   0.2   1

2 Fill in the missing numbers on the number lines. The first one has been done for you.

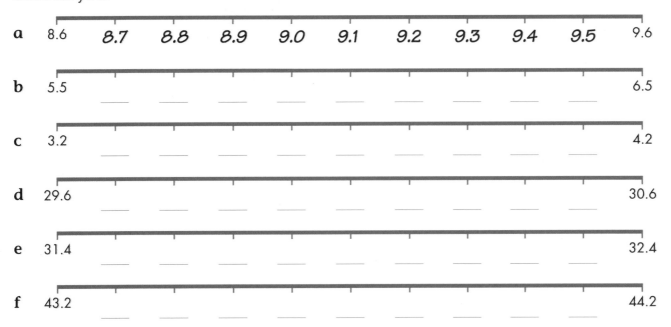

a   8.6   *8.7*   *8.8*   *8.9*   *9.0*   *9.1*   *9.2*   *9.3*   *9.4*   *9.5*   9.6

b   5.5   6.5

c   3.2   4.2

d   29.6   30.6

e   31.4   32.4

f   43.2   44.2

3 Order these groups of decimal fractions from the smallest to the largest.

a   6.3   7.3   2.6   5.6   7.6 _____

b   6.8   9.2   9.7   5.2   5.8 _____

c   14.8   13.6   14   13   14.3 _____

d   78.1   87.2   78.3   87.4   88.2 _____

e   22.6   26.7   25.1   23.2   28.1 _____

f   22.6   22.5   19.2   20.1   28.2 _____

Exercise 5A Mode

This exercise will give you practice in
- making and using a simple database
- finding the mode of a set of data

1 The two tables show test scores for 10 Year 7 students in Maths and English.

Maths

Darren	9
Navdeep	8
Zarin	6
Hayley	2
Ross	8
Lianne	5
Rahat	5
Jeevan	10
Clinton	8
Tanika	6

English

Darren	7
Navdeep	10
Zarin	7
Hayley	10
Ross	3
Lianne	6
Rahat	8
Jeevan	7
Clinton	4
Tanika	8

a Complete the database below.

Name	Maths test score	English test score
Darren	9	7
Navdeep	8	

b What is the lowest Maths score?

c What is the highest English score?

_____

d Which students scored 8 in the English test?

_____

e How many students scored more than 6 in the Maths test?

_____

f Which students did better in the English test than the Maths test?

_____

g What is the mode for the English test?

_____

h What is the mode for the Maths test?

_____

2 This database contains information about a group of Year 7 students.

Name	Way of travelling to school	Time to travel to school (minutes)	Distance travelled to school (kilometres)
Charlotte	bus	20	2
Anoop	bus	15	$1\frac{1}{2}$
Peter	cycle	10	1
Amrat	car	15	2
Paula	walk	5	$\frac{1}{2}$
Devan	walk	10	$\frac{1}{2}$
Steven	bus	15	2

a What is the longest travel time?

_____

b Which students live $\frac{1}{2}$ km from school?

_____

c How does Anoop travel to school?

_____

d What is the most common way of travelling to school?

_____

e **i** What is the most common distance travelled?_____

    ii What is this number called? _____

f What is the mode for the time taken? _____

g How many students travel for longer than 10 minutes?_____

Exercise 5B   Frequency tables and pictograms

This exercise will give you practice in

- using data from a frequency table to complete a pictogram, and vice versa
- interpreting pictograms and frequency tables

A group of Year 7 students voted for their favourite chocolate bar. The results are shown in the frequency table on the right.

Chocolate bar	Frequency
Snickers	8
Flake	12
Mars Bar	14
Twix	7

1 Complete the pictogram using ☺ to represent two chocolate bars.

Favourite chocolate bar

Snickers

Flake

Mars Bar

Twix

Key: _____

2 How many students voted for Flake? _____

3 What is the frequency for Twix? _____

This frequency table shows how many bars of chocolate were eaten in a month by the same Year 7 students.

Chocolate bar	Frequency
Twix	10
Flake	35
Mars Bar	40
Snickers	12

4 Complete the pictogram using ☺ to represent five chocolate bars.

Number of chocolate bars eaten in a month

Twix

Flake

Mars Bar

Snickers

Key: _____

5 How many Snickers were eaten? _____

6 What is the frequency for Mars Bars? _____

Exercise 5C   Probability

This exercise will give you practice in
○ deciding how certain or likely particular events are

1 Draw a line to match up the words on the left to the ones that mean the same on the right. There may be more than one answer for each!

unlikely	high chance
	no chance
impossible	poor chance
	low chance
certain	must happen
	cannot happen
likely	good chance

2 How likely are these events to happen. Write the correct word next to each event.

  unlikely   **impossible**   **certain**   **likely**

  a You will hand all of your homework in on time _____

  b You will win the Lottery if you buy a ticket _____

  c You will get older _____

  d This lesson will end _____

  e You will be in Year 11 next year _____

  f You will win Pop Idol 2009 if you enter _____

3 Look at these events.

  A   You will be one year older next year

  B   You will grow another head

  C   You will meet David Beckham

  D   You will see your form tutor next week

Place the letter for each of the events where you think it should go on this scale.

no chance	poor chance	good chance	certain

Exercise 5D   Bar charts 1

This exercise will give you practice in

  ● solving problems by representing data in and reading data from a bar chart

Sally and Tim surveyed their class on eye colour. They recorded their results in the tally chart on the right.

1 Fill in the frequency column.

Eye Colour	Tally	Frequency
Blue	⊬⊬⊬ |||	
Green	⊬⊬⊬ ||	
Brown	⊬⊬⊬ ⊬⊬⊬		
Grey	||	
Other			

2 Complete the bar chart.

3 How many students have green eyes?

_____

4 Which is the most common eye colour?

_____

5 How many students were surveyed in total?

_____

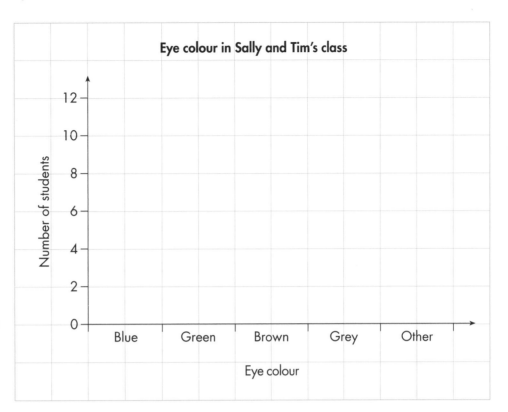

Exercise 5E Bar charts 2

This exercise will give you practice in

- solving problems by representing data in and reading data from a bar chart

Alex asked six of his friends how much television they had watched, in minutes, one evening. The results are shown in the frequency table on the right.

Name	Amount of television watched (minutes)
Raj	20
Stephan	75
Kylie	30
Gemma	20
Sunil	0
Craig	60

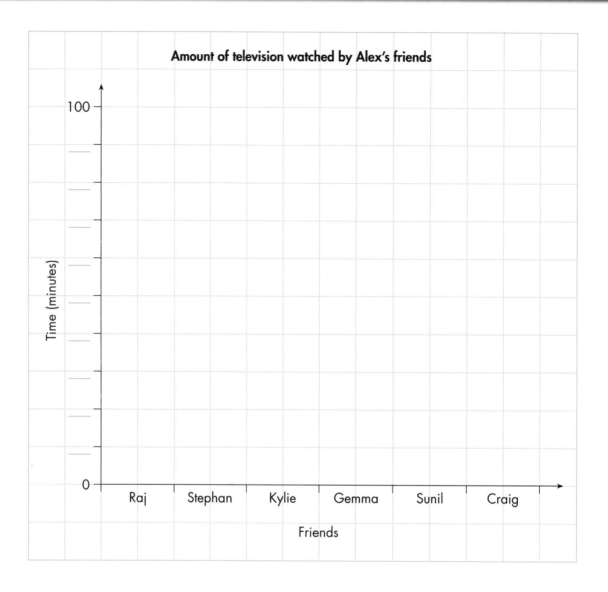

1 Write in the scale for time in the spaces provided.

2 Complete the bar chart using the data in the frequency table.

3 Who watched the most television? _____

4 Who watched the least television? _____

5 What is the most common amount of television watched? _____

6 What is the answer to **Question 5** called? _____

Exercise 6A Ordering decimal fractions

This exercise will give you practice in
- using decimal notation for tenths and hundredths
- ordering decimal fractions with the same number of decimal places

1 Write the hundredths from 0 to 0.1 as decimal fractions.

0   0.01   0.02   0.1

2 Fill in missing numbers on the number lines. The first one has been done for you.

a 8.4   *8.41   8.42   8.43   8.44   8.45   8.46   8.47   8.48   8.49*   8.5

b 5.5   5.6

c 31.4   31.5

d 5.5   5.6

e 42.3   42.4

f 18   18.1

3 Order these groups of decimal fractions from smallest to largest.

  a 7.56   7.65   7.55   7.60   7.50   _____

  b 18.03   19.30   19.04   20.15   18.40   _____

  c 27.34   27.65   27.56   27.43   27.50   _____

d   46.02   46.09   64.23   46.29   46.12   _____

e   33.88   33.77   33.99   33.66   33.55   _____

f   22.34   22.43   22.36   22.63   22.90   _____

Exercise 6B   Finding the difference

This exercise will give you practice in

○ finding the difference between pairs of decimal fractions

1 Use the number lines to find the difference between each pair of decimals.
The first one has been done for you.

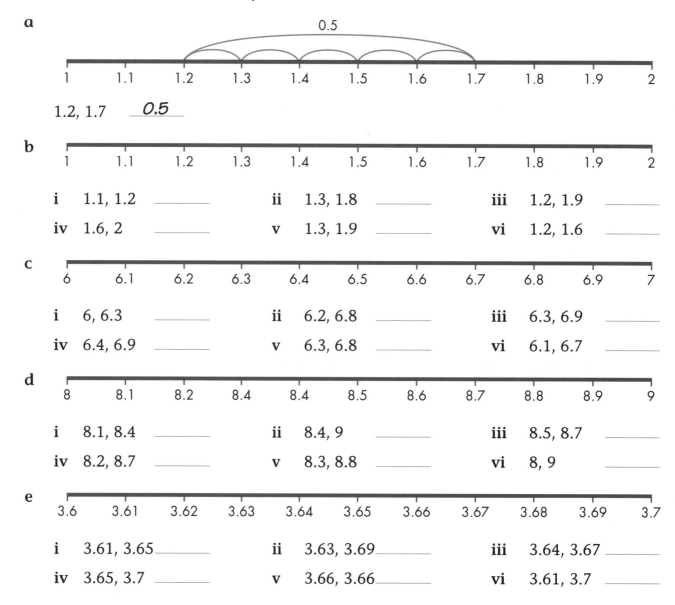

a

1.2, 1.7   _0.5_

b

i   1.1, 1.2 _____   ii   1.3, 1.8 _____   iii 1.2, 1.9 _____

iv   1.6, 2   _____   v   1.3, 1.9 _____   vi   1.2, 1.6 _____

c

i   6, 6.3   _____   ii   6.2, 6.8 _____   iii 6.3, 6.9 _____

iv   6.4, 6.9 _____   v   6.3, 6.8 _____   vi   6.1, 6.7 _____

d

i   8.1, 8.4 _____   ii   8.4, 9   _____   iii 8.5, 8.7 _____

iv   8.2, 8.7 _____   v   8.3, 8.8 _____   vi   8, 9   _____

e

i   3.61, 3.65_____   ii   3.63, 3.69_____   iii 3.64, 3.67 _____

iv   3.65, 3.7 _____   v   3.66, 3.66_____   vi   3.61, 3.7 _____

f

| 12.9 | 12.91 | 12.92 | 12.93 | 12.94 | 12.95 | 12.96 | 12.97 | 12.98 | 12.99 | 13 |

   i   12.93, 12.99 _____   ii   12.9, 12.94 _____   iii   12.96, 13 _____

   iv 12, 13 _____   v   12.92, 12.98 _____   vi   12.91, 13 _____

Exercise 6C   Rounding decimals

This exercise will give you practice in

- rounding decimals with one or two decimal places to the nearest integer

1 Write down the two whole numbers that each decimal comes between. Circle the number that the decimal is closest to. The first one has been done for you.

a   _6_   6.8   ⑦ _____   b _____ 5.2 _____

c _____ 3.6 _____   d _____ 4.9 _____

e _____ 5.5 _____   f _____ 23.2 _____

g _____ 19.6 _____   h _____ 1.2 _____

i _____ 7.5 _____   j _____ 3.23 _____

k _____ 17.51 _____   l _____ 34.76 _____

m _____ 49.99 _____

2 Using the digit cards below, write down 10 numbers to one or two decimal places. Then round them to the nearest whole number.

_____ _____   _____ _____

_____ _____   _____ _____

_____ _____   _____ _____

_____ _____   _____ _____

Exercise 6D   Equivalence

This exercise will give you practice in
- relating fractions to their decimal equivalents and vice versa

1 Join each of the decimals to its fractional partner with a line.

0.5	$\frac{1}{10}$
0.1	$\frac{8}{10}$
0.8	$\frac{3}{10}$
0.25	$\frac{1}{2}$
0.6	$\frac{9}{10}$
0.9	$\frac{6}{10}$
0.3	$\frac{4}{10}$
0.75	$\frac{3}{4}$
0.4	$\frac{1}{4}$

2 Convert these decimals to their mixed fraction equivalents.

a   2.1 _____   b   9.2 _____   c   8.4 _____

d   5.6 _____   e   7.3 _____   f   4.9 _____

g   5.5 _____   h   1.7 _____   i   3.8 _____

3 Convert these mixed fractions to their decimal equivalents.

a $22\frac{2}{10}$ _____   b $33\frac{3}{10}$ _____   c $25\frac{5}{10}$ _____

d $12\frac{1}{2}$ _____   e $15\frac{1}{4}$ _____

Exercise 6E   Solving problems

This exercise will give you practice in

- solving word problems involving decimals

1 Year 7 is selling tickets for the end of term concert. Each ticket costs £2.50. The hall can hold up to 500 people. How much money will the school make if the hall is full on the day of the concert?

Problem

Calculation

Answer to calculation

Answer to problem

Exercise 7A Angles

This exercise will give you practice in
- identifying obtuse, acute and right angles
- beginning to apply these terms to triangles

1 Circle the lines that form angles.

a  b  c  d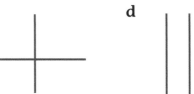

2 In what unit do we measure angles? _____

3 Circle the lines which form acute angles.

a  b  c  d

4 Circle the lines which form obtuse angles.

a 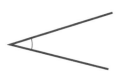 b  c  d

5 Circle the lines which form right angles.

a 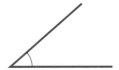 b  c   d

6 In the spaces provided, write down which angle in each of the triangles is an obtuse angle, an acute angle or a right angle. Remember that some triangles may not contain any obtuse angles or right angles!

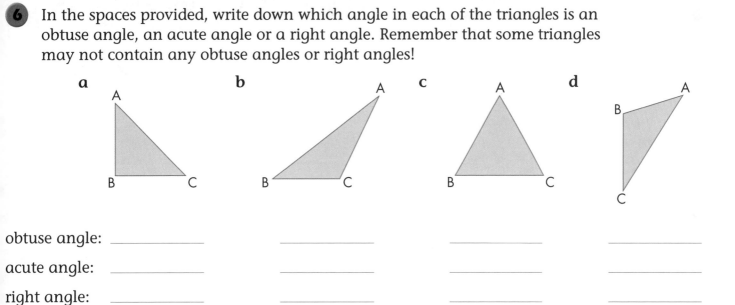

a   b   c   d

obtuse angle: _____ _____ _____ _____

acute angle: _____ _____ _____ _____

right angle: _____ _____ _____ _____

Exercise 7B   Classifying triangles

This exercise will give you practice in

- classifying triangles according to the properties of their sides and angles

1 **a**, **b**, **c** and **d** are four isosceles triangles. Circle the two angles that are the same in each triangle.

a   b   c   d

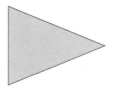

2 Which of these triangles are isosceles triangles?

a   b   c   d

3 Which of the triangles below are scalene triangles?

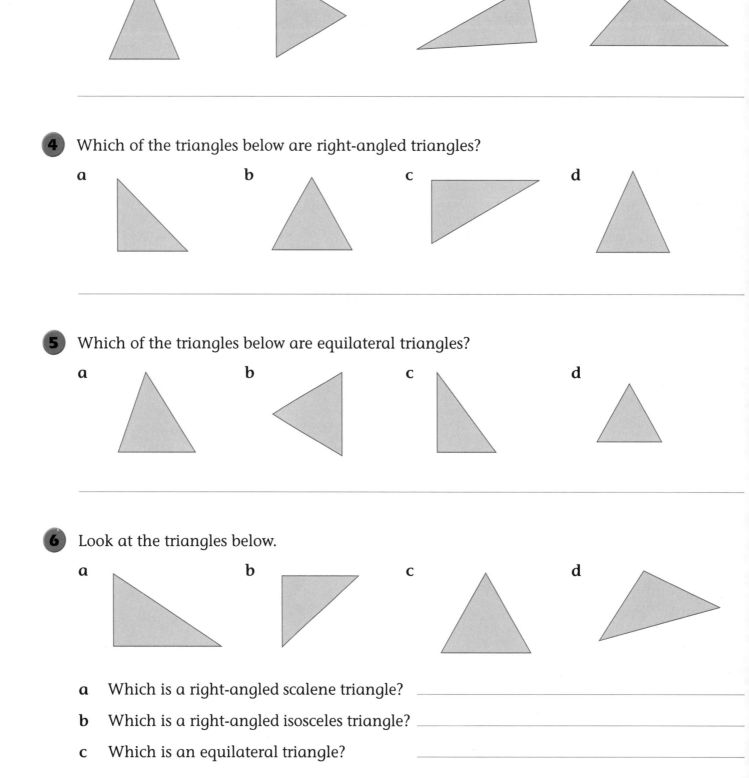

a   b   c   d

4 Which of the triangles below are right-angled triangles?

a   b   c   d

5 Which of the triangles below are equilateral triangles?

a   b   c   d

6 Look at the triangles below.

a   b   c   d

a   Which is a right-angled scalene triangle? _____

b   Which is a right-angled isosceles triangle? _____

c   Which is an equilateral triangle? _____

7 Draw in any lines of symmetry for each of the following triangles.

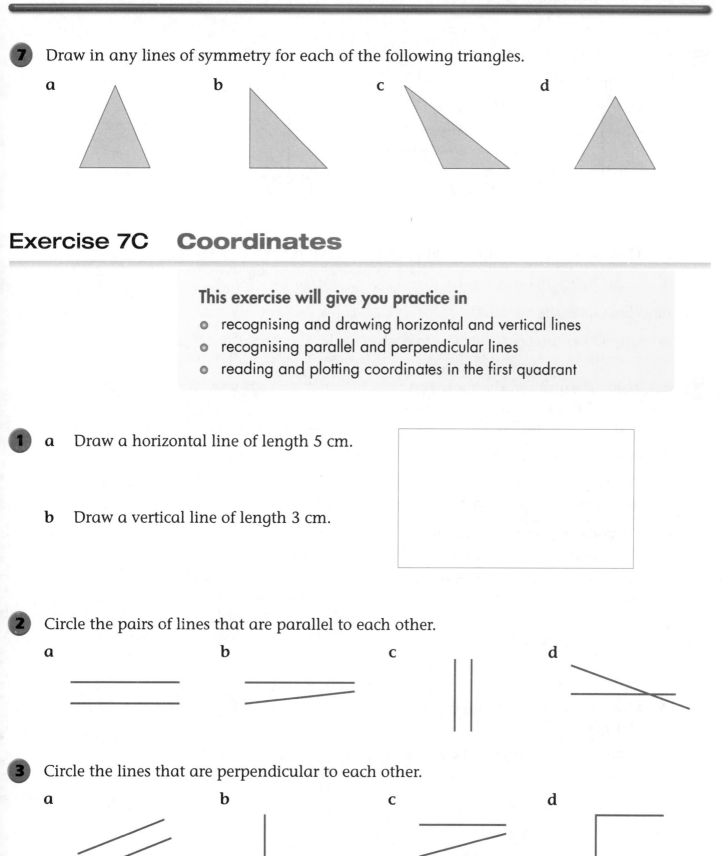

a   b   c   d

Exercise 7C   Coordinates

This exercise will give you practice in

- recognising and drawing horizontal and vertical lines
- recognising parallel and perpendicular lines
- reading and plotting coordinates in the first quadrant

1 **a** Draw a horizontal line of length 5 cm.

b Draw a vertical line of length 3 cm.

2 Circle the pairs of lines that are parallel to each other.

a   b   c   d

3 Circle the lines that are perpendicular to each other.

a   b   c   d

4 For each of the sets of lines shown (**a**, **b**, **c** and **d**), write down whether each of the statements is true (T) or false (F).

a   **b**   **c**   **d**

		a	b	c	d
i	These lines are horizontal and parallel to each other.	___	___	___	___
ii	These lines are horizontal.	___	___	___	___
iii	These lines are parallel.	___	___	___	___
iv	These lines are perpendicular to each other.	___	___	___	___

5 **a** Write in x and y in the spaces on the grid to show which is the x-axis and which is the y-axis.

b Place an X at the origin (0,0)

c On the grid plot the following points.
A(0,1) B(1,5) C(3,5) D(3,7) E(4,2)

d On your grid, join the two points that make a horizontal line.

e On your grid, join the two points that make a vertical line.

f Are your two lines perpendicular to each other?

_____

g Draw a line on your grid to make a triangle.

h What sort of triangle have you drawn?

_____

Exercise 8A   Tally charts and frequency tables

This exercise will give you practice in

● creating and using tally charts and frequency tables

The table below shows a survey of the type of television programmes a group of Year 12 students enjoy most.

Type of programme	Tally	Frequency
Soap operas	⊥⊥⊥⊥ ⊥⊥⊥⊥ ⊥⊥⊥⊥ ⊥⊥⊥⊥ ⊥⊥⊥⊥ |||	
Comedy	⊥⊥⊥⊥ ⊥⊥⊥⊥ |||	
The news	⊥⊥⊥⊥ ||	
Reality TV	⊥⊥⊥⊥ ⊥⊥⊥⊥ ⊥⊥⊥⊥	
Drama	⊥⊥⊥⊥ ⊥⊥⊥⊥		
Documentaries	⊥⊥⊥⊥ ⊥⊥⊥⊥ ||	

1 Count up the tally marks and fill in the frequency column.

2 **a** Which is the most popular type of programme? _____

   b How many people voted for this? _____

3 **a** Which is the least popular type of programme? _____

   b How many people voted for this? _____

4 How many people enjoy drama programmes the most? _____

5 How many people enjoy comedy programmes the most? _____

6 How many more people chose soap operas than
drama as their favourite type of programme? _____

Exercise 8B   Mode and range

This exercise will give you practice in
- finding the mode and range for a set of data

1 Twenty people were stopped in the street and asked their age. The results are shown below.

15, 27, 30, 56, 72, 30, 42, 17, 21, 64, 30, 17, 36, 39, 19, 30, 41, 43, 22, 53

a   Place the ages in order from youngest to eldest. (You may want to use a pencil!)

_____

_____

b   What is the mode of the ages? _____

c   What is the range of the ages? _____

2 Find the mode and range for both of the following sets of data, sorting the data first.

a   2, 5, 6, 8, 8, 6, 7, 7, 4, 9, 1, 1, 3, 2, 4, 8, 9, 8

Sort the data: _____

_____

Mode: _____   Range: _____

b   23, 22, 28, 21, 21, 29, 22, 25, 24, 22, 27, 28

Sort the data: _____

_____

Mode: _____   Range: _____

3 The database shows some of the results of the school tennis club.

Name	Won	Lost	Drawn
Sharon	2	1	3
Sophie	4	0	0
Keon	3	1	0
Raj	2	1	1
Joely	2	0	2
Jack	3	1	1
Angela	1	3	0
Steven	1	2	1

a How many games did Keon lose? _____

b How many games did Sophie win? _____

c How many games did Angela draw? _____

d What is the mode for the number of games lost? _____

e What is the mode for the number of games won? _____

f What was the total number of games lost? _____

g Which two players won and lost the same number of games? _____

Exercise 8C   Carroll diagrams

This exercise will give you practice in

- putting data into Carroll diagrams and using it to solve problems

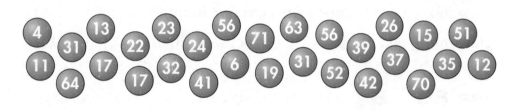

	Red	Blue
Less than 30	◯	◯
More than 30	◯	◯

1 **a** Write each number in the correct space on the Carroll diagram.

b Count the numbers in each space on the Carroll diagram. Write the totals in the circle.

c How many numbers are 30 or more? _____

d How many blue numbers are less than 30? _____

e How many reds are there all together? _____

	Odd	Even
Between 20 and 50	○	○
Not between 20 and 50	○	○

2 Look at the numbers again.

a Write each number in the correct space on this Carroll diagram.

b Count the numbers in each space on the Carroll diagram.
Write the totals in the circle.

c How many odd numbers are there? _____

d How many numbers are between 20 and 50? _____

e How many even numbers are between 20 and 50? _____

f How many odd numbers are not between 20 and 50? _____

Exercise 8D   Bar-line charts

This exercise will give you practice in

- using data from tally charts and frequency tables to complete bar-line charts
- reading data from bar-line charts

Navdeep recorded the number of different coloured cars that drove past her house one Saturday afternoon for a school project. She recorded her results in a tally chart.

Colour	Number of cars	Frequency
Red	ЖЖ IIII	
Black	ЖЖ ЖЖ III	
Blue	ЖЖ II	
Silver	III	
Green	ЖЖ	
White	ЖЖ III	

1 Write the frequencies on the table.

2 Complete the bar-line chart.

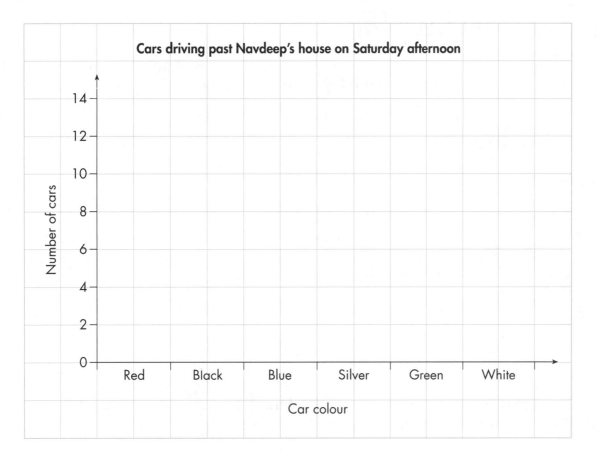

Cars driving past Navdeep's house on Saturday afternoon

Number of cars

14
12
10
8
6
4
2
0

Red   Black   Blue   Silver   Green   White

Car colour

3 Which colour car drove past Navdeep's house the most? _____

4 What is this number called? _____

5 How many blue cars drove past Navdeep's house? _____

6 How many cars drove past Navdeep's house in total? _____

7 How many of the cars that drove past Navdeep's house were not black? _____

Exercise 9A   Multiplication

This exercise will give you practice in
- using and learning multiplication facts

1 Complete each of the following calculations.

a $7 \times 4 =$ _____

b $4 \times 9 =$ _____

c $7 \times 3 =$ _____

d $4 \times 6 =$ _____

e $7 \times 9 =$ _____

f $8 \times 6 =$ _____

g $9 \times 8 =$ _____

h   _____ $\times 6 = 42$

i $5 \times$ _____ $= 45$

j $8 \times$ _____ $= 56$

k   _____ $\times$ _____ $= 24$

l   _____ $\times$ _____ $= 48$

m   _____ $\times$ _____ $= 36$

2 Some of these calculations are incorrect. Find the incorrect calculations and write the correct calculation underneath each one.

$2 \times 45 = 180$ $3 \times 40 = 120$ $4 \times 50 = 250$ $5 \times 25 = 125$

_____   _____   _____   _____

$6 \times 20 = 120$ $5 \times 50 = 250$ $3 \times 27 = 63$

_____   _____   _____

$6 \times 40 = 240$ $3 \times 15 = 60$

_____   _____

$7 \times 21 = 147$ $4 \times 80 = 320$ $5 \times 40 = 200$

_____   _____   _____

$6 \times 30 = 160$

_____

3 Complete the multiplication grid.

×	4	8	1	10
3	12	24	3	30
8				
6		48		
9				90
5	20		5	
1				
7				

Exercise 9B   Division

This exercise will give you practice in
- using and learning division facts

1 Complete each of the following calculations.

a $32 \div 8 =$ _____

b $24 \div 4 =$ _____

c $27 \div 3 =$ _____

d $56 \div 7 =$ _____

e $72 \div 8 =$ _____

f $30 \div 5 =$ _____

g $80 \div 10 =$ _____

h $60 \div 5 =$ _____

i _____ $\div 3 = 5$

j $24 \div$ _____ $= 4$

k $32 \div$ _____ $= 8$

l $64 \div$ _____ $= 8$

m $54 \div$ _____ $= 6$

2 Work out the division facts. Draw a line to the matching multiplication fact.

a $24 \div 6 =$ _____ 4×8

b $32 \div 4 =$ _____ 9×3

c $27 \div 3 =$ _____ 4×4

d $20 \div 4 =$ _____ 3×6

e $18 \div 6 =$ _____ 7×4

f $16 \div 4 =$ _____ 6×4

g $28 \div 7 =$ _____ 5×4

Exercise 9C   Brackets

This exercise will give you practice in

○ using brackets in calculations

1 Complete the table below by following the example given and the steps below.

- write the number sentence in the first column
- decide which order to complete the calculations
- write the calculations in the order you do them
- work out the answer

An example

	Number sentence	First calculation	Next calculation	Answer
Example	$(3 + 6) \times 5$	$3 + 6 = 9$	9×5	45
a				
b				
c				
d				
e				
f				
g				
h				

a $3 \times (2 + 5)$ **b** $(17 + 23) \div 4$ **c** $35 \div (5 + 2)$ **d** $(4 + 2) \times 5$

e $(10 + 14) \div 3$ **f** $14 \div (2 + 5)$ **g** $7 \times (6 - 4)$ **h** $(8 - 4) \div 2$

2 Put in the brackets to make these calculations correct.

a $3 \times 40 - 20 = 60$ **b** $5 \times 20 \div 10 = 10$ **c** $3 + 6 - 1 \div 4 = 2$

d $32 + 8 \div 4 = 10$ **e** $36 \div 6 - 3 = 12$ **f** $5 \times 5 + 8 = 65$

Exercise 9D   BODMAS

This exercise will give you practice in

○ using BODMAS, the order of operations

B	– Brackets
O	– pOwers
DM	– Division and Multiplication
AS	– Addition and Subtraction

1 Write the short form for the following square numbers.

a 3×3 _____

b 4×4 _____

c 5×5 _____

d 6×6 _____

e 7×7 _____

f 8×8 _____

2 Complete the table below by following the example given and the steps below.
- write the number sentence in the first column
- decide which order to complete the calculations
- write the calculations in the order you do them
- work out the answer

	Number sentence	First calculation	Next calculation	Next calculation	Answer
Example	$5 + 3 \times 4 + 2^2$	$2^2 = 4$	$3 \times 4 = 12$	$5 + 12 + 4$	21
a					
b					
c					
d					
e					

a $6 + 4 \times 6 + 3^2$

b $2^2 + 17 + 24 \div 4$

c $35 \div 5 + 7 + 3^2$

d $4 + 2^2 \times 2$

e $(10 + 14) \div 3 + 5^2$

f $10 + 4 \div 2 + 3^2$

g $4 \times 3 - 5 + 5^2$

h $19 + (10 - 4) \times 6$

i $(30 - 8) \div 2 + 4$

Exercise 10A Doubling and halving

This exercise will give you practice in
- doubling and halving in calculations

1 Double each of the following numbers.

| 24 | 62 | 34 | 66 | 55 | 28 | 72 | 80 | 45 |

2 Halve each of the following numbers.

| 128 | 136 | 150 | 144 | 194 | 156 | 178 | 182 |

3 The rule for $\times 50$ is first $\times 100$ then $\div 2$. Use this rule to calculate the answer to each of the following questions. The first one has been done for you.

a 18×50
$(18 \times 100) \div 2 = 1800 \div 2 = 900$

b 26×50

c 44×50

d 14×50

e 37×50

f 46×50

g 16×50

h 19×50

i 34×50

j 29×50

Exercise 10B Estimation

This exercise will give you practice in

- rounding integers to the nearest 10
- rounding decimals to the nearest integer
- estimating calculations by approximation

1 Write the approximation to the nearest 10 for each of the following numbers. The first one has been done for you.

a 154 _154 ≈ 150_   b 122 _____   c 166 _____

d 235 _____   e 288 _____   f 299 _____

g 323 _____   h 355 _____   i 363 _____

j 402 _____   k 408 _____   l 555 _____

m 582 _____

2 Write the approximation to the nearest whole number for each of the following.

a 23.24 _____   b 21.55 _____   c 44.87 _____

d 32.43 _____   e 55.47 _____   f 56.54 _____

g 77.29 _____   h 83.57 _____   i 89.99 _____

j 91.24 _____   k 94.11 _____   l 96.52 _____

m 98.38 _____

3 Approximate the answer to each calculation. The first one has been done for you.

a 37×19 _$37 \times 19 \approx 40 \times 20 = 800$_   b 12×29 _____

c 22×38 _____   d 34×17 _____

e 42×44 _____   f 14×45 _____

g 38×48 _____

4 Check your approximations in **Question 3** by working out the answers using your calculator.

a _____   b _____   c _____   d _____

e _____   f _____   g _____

Exercise 10C Rounding after division

This exercise will give you practice in
- finding remainders after division
- using division to solve word problems
- rounding up or down after division

1 Find the answers to these division problems. Work out your answers on rough paper and write the answer in the box. Watch out – some of them have remainders!

a $24 \div 3$ ☐   b $32 \div 4$ ☐

c $42 \div 5$ ☐   d $54 \div 9$ ☐

e $36 \div 9$ ☐   f $47 \div 4$ ☐

g $72 \div 8$ ☐   h $25 \div 3$ ☐

i $16 \div 2$ ☐   j $43 \div 4$ ☐

2 The Big Dipper seats 8 people per carriage. There are 240 people in the queue. How many carriages will be needed?

3 Bread rolls are sold in packs of 6. A batch of dough makes 286 bread rolls. How many packs of bread rolls can be made up out of 1 batch of dough?

4 Class 7A are going on a school trip in minibuses. There are 37 students in Class 7A and each minibus can hold 8 students. How many minibuses will be needed?

Exercise 10D Solving money problems

This exercise will give you practice in

- using division to solve real-life problems involving money

1 Divide these amounts in pounds by the numbers given. Give your answers in pence.

    a £1 ÷ 2 _____

    b £1 ÷ 4 _____

    c £1 ÷ 10 _____

    d £4 ÷ 5 _____

    e £3 ÷ 4 _____

    f £2 ÷ 5 _____

    g £5 ÷ 10 _____

2 Five Year 7 classes were given £200 by the head teacher to spend on their Christmas party. How much did each class receive? Show your working.

3 Four friends went out carol singing and collected £17. If they shared the money equally between them, how much did each one receive? Show your working.

4 Three local businesses donated a total of £256.50 to a school. Given that each business donated the same amount, how much did each donate? Show your working.

5 The ICT department bought six identical printers at a total cost of £421.50. How much did each printer cost?

Exercise 10E   More money problems

This exercise will give you practice in

○ using multiplication and addition to solve real-life problems involving money

1 Use your calculator to find the total cost of each set of items. Write down your calculation

a   two pairs of trainers and a CD Walkman

b   two mobile phones and three pairs of trainers

c   three CD Walkmans, a pair of trainers and a stereo

d   three pairs of trainers, two CD Walkmans and a mobile phone

2 Use your calculator to find the total cost of each set of items. Write down your calculation.

a   a CD and two chocolate bars

b   two CDs and two DVDs

c   five CDs, two videos and a chocolate bar

d   two DVDs, three CDs and two chocolate bars

e   three of each item

3 Using the information from **Question 2**, answer each of the following questions.

    a   How much more does a DVD cost than a video tape?

_____

    b   How much more does a video tape cost than ten chocolate bars?

_____

    c   How much more does it cost to buy two CDs rather than one DVD?

_____

    d   How much more do two DVDs cost than two CDs?

_____

Exercise 10F   Capacity

This exercise will give you practice in

- using and writing measures of capacity such as *l* and *ml*÷

1 Draw a line between the two capacities that are the same.
Circle the odd one out.

250 ml

0.75 l

750 ml

Lemonade 2 l

Fizzy Pop 330 ml

Fruit Drink 0.33 l

0.25 l

NATURAL SPRING WATER 2000 ml

0.5 l

2 A Year 7 class were going on a school trip. They bought the following drinks.

NATURAL SPRING WATER 2000 ml

COKE 330 ml

WATER 250 ml

FRESH ORANGE 1000 ml

Fruit Drink 200 ml

Coke 1500 ml

APPLE JUICE 150 ml

a Change the capacity from millilitres into litres. Record your answers in decimal form in the space provided.

b What is the capacity of two cans of coke and two cartons of orange juice? Record your answer in millilitres and litres. _____

_____

c What is the capacity of three cartons of apple juice and two cartons of fruit drink? Write your answer in millilitres and litres. _____

_____

d What is the capacity of all the drinks in total? Write your answer in millilitres and litres. _____

_____

Exercise 10G Weight

This exercise will give you practice in

○ using and writing units of mass such as kg and g

1 Write these weights in grams. The first one has been done for you.

a $5\frac{1}{2}$ kg   *= 5000 g + 500 g = 5500 g*

b $3\frac{1}{4}$ kg   _____

c $6\frac{1}{5}$ kg _____

d $4\frac{1}{10}$ kg _____

2 Write these weights in kilograms and grams. The first one has been done for you.

a 6500 g *= 6000 g + 500 g = 6 kg 500 g* _____

b 3256 g _____

c 7560 g _____

d 4700 g _____

e 6640 g _____

3 Choose three standard weights to balance each of the following totals. The first one has been done for you.

a 530 g *= 500 g + 20 g + 10 g* _____

b 720 g _____

c 270 g _____

d 570 g _____

e 80 g _____

4 Choose four standard weights to balance these totals.

a 1800 g _____

b 330 g _____

c 1350 g _____

d 1080 g _____

Exercise 10H Time

> **This exercise will give you practice in**
> - converting between 12- and 24-hour clock times

1 Write the 24-hour times for each of the following. The first one has been done for you.

a   3:00 pm _15:00_   b   9:45 pm _____

c   10:35 pm _____   d   9:30 am _____

e   11:52 pm _____   f   2:56 pm _____

2 Write the 12-hour times for each of the following.

a   19:00   _____

b   14:54   _____

c   16:45   _____

d   15:25   _____

e   09:45   _____

f   13:56   _____

3 Complete the chart.

Time	12-hour clock	24-hour clock
Half past 6 in the morning	6:30 am	06:30
		14:35
	8:30 pm	
Quarter to 10 in the evening		
		07:45
	2:45 am	
		23:50
Half past midnight		
	3:45 pm	
		02:50

Exercise 11A Classifying and ordering angles

This exercise will give you practice in

- identifing and ordering acute, obtuse and reflex angles

1 Circle the acute angles.

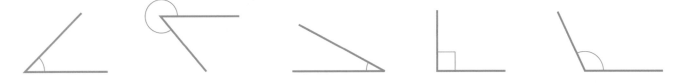

2 Circle the obtuse angles.

3 Circle the reflex angles.

4 Write down the order of these acute angles from smallest to largest.

a   b   c   d

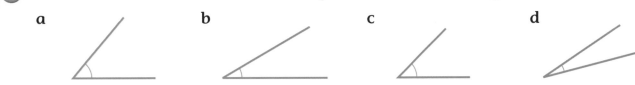

5 Write down the order of these obtuse angles from smallest to largest.

a   b   c   d

6 Write down the order of these reflex angles from smallest to largest.

a  b  c  d

Exercise 11B   Measuring and drawing angles

This exercise will give you practice in
- measuring and drawing angles using a protractor

1 Using a protractor, measure these acute angles.

a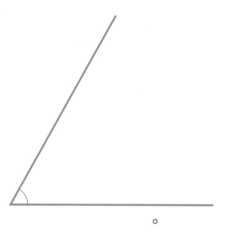

b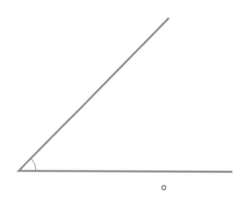

°
_____

°
_____

c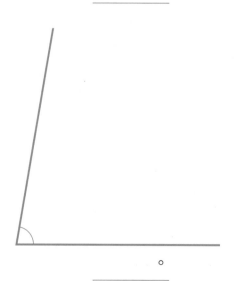

d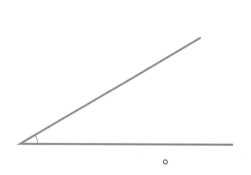

°
_____

°
_____

2 Using a protractor, measure these obtuse angles.

a

b

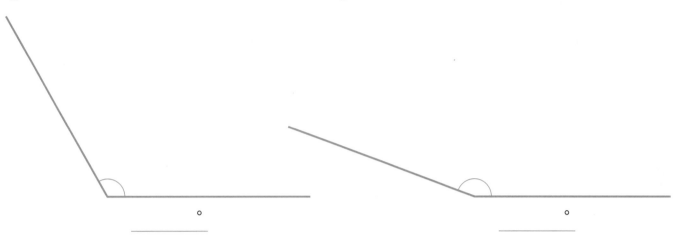

°

°

c

d

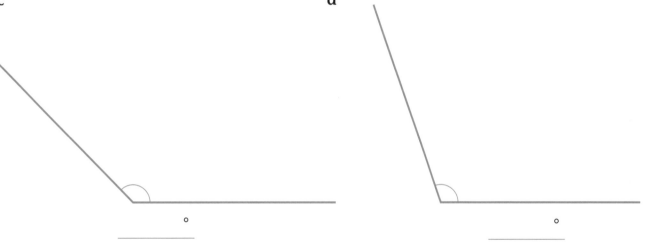

°

°

3 Using a protractor, measure these reflex angles.

a

b

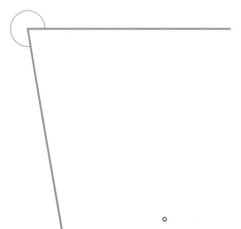

°

°

c 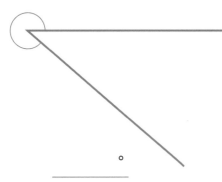 d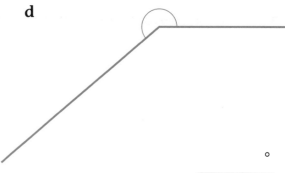

4. Starting from the left-hand side of the line, draw the following angles and write down if they are acute or obtuse.

a   45°   b   60°   c   120°   d   160°

a _____

b _____

c _____

d _____

5 Starting from the right-hand side of the line, draw the following angles and write down if they are acute or obtuse.

a   130°   b   30°   c   70°   d   100°

a   ——————————

b   ——————————

c   ——————————

d   ——————————

Exercise 11C Solving geometric problems

This exercise will give you practice in

- recognising properties of rectangles and other polygons, such as parallel sides and right angles

Some of the sides and diagonals are missing from these shapes.

a

b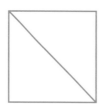

c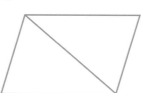

d

e

f

g

h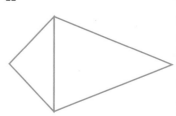

1 Complete the shapes and draw in any missing diagonals.

2 Mark in the right angles on the shapes.

3 Which shapes do not have four right angles? _____

4 Which shapes are rectangles? _____

5 Which shapes are squares? _____

6 Which shapes are not made up of parallel lines? _____

69

Exercise 12A **Percentages**

This exercise will give you practice in

- understanding and using percentages

1 Look at the grids and write down what fraction and what percentage of each grid is shaded.

a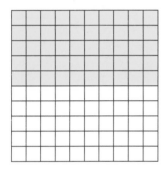

_____

b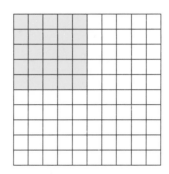

_____

c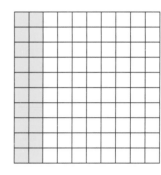

_____

d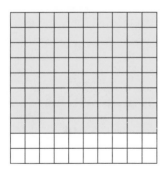

_____

e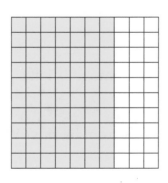

_____

f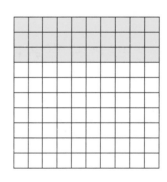

_____

g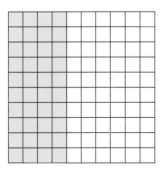

_____

h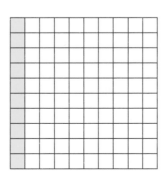

_____

i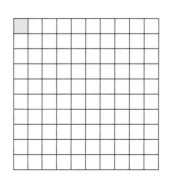

_____

Exercise 12B Percentages of quantities

This exercise will give you practice in
○ finding percentages of whole number quantities

1 Work out each of the following. Show your working.

a   50% of 100 kg

b   50% of £10

c   50% of 10 cm

d   50% of £1

e   50% of 10 mm

f   25% of £1

g   25% of 100 kg

h   25% of 10 cm

i   10% of 100 kg

j   10% of £1

k   10% of 10 mm

2 Solve the percentage problems.

a   I eat 50% of my pizza. What percentage is left?

b   70% of Year 7 students travel to school by bus? What percentage do not travel to school by bus?

c   If 90% of your homework was correct, what percentage did you get wrong?

3 Work out each of the following. Show your working.

a   50% of £30

b   50% of 150 m

c   50% of £22

d   25% of £40

e   25% of 60 kg _____

f   25% of £20 _____

g   10% of £160 _____

h   10% of 180 cm _____

i   10% of £50 _____

Exercise 12C Ratio and proportion

This exercise will give you practice in

o using ratio and proportion

1 Complete each of the following tables.

a   For every £1 that James spends on holiday, his sister, Claire spends £4. Complete the table showing how much they spend.

James	Claire
£1	£4
£2	

b   For every two boys in the class, there are three girls. Complete the table showing the boys and girls in the class.

Boys	Girls
2	3
4	

c   For every two apples that Eddie eats, Jill eats four. Complete the table showing how many apples they eat.

Eddie	Jill
2	4
4	

2 The wine gums I buy always have two orange ones for every four red ones.

Orange	Red
2	4

   a Complete the table for the number of red and orange wine gums.

   b What is the ratio of orange wine gums to red wine gums?

   c How many red wine gums would I have eaten if I had eaten 14 orange wine gums?

   d How many orange wine gums would I have eaten if I had eaten 28 red wine gums?

Exercise 12D Solving problems with ratio and proportion

This exercise will give you practice in

○ using ratio and proportion to solve problems

1 Complete the tables to help you solve the problems.

   a Raj's mum made 16 cakes. For every cake Raj ate, his mum ate 3.

Raj	Raj's mum	Total cakes
1	3	4

      i How many cakes did Raj eat?

      ii How many cakes did his mum eat?

b A family drinks one glass of still water for two glasses of fizzy water. One weekend they drank 21 glasses of water.

Still water	Fizzy water	Total water
1	2	3

   i How many glasses of still water did they drink?

     _____

   ii How many glasses of fizzy water did they drink?

     _____

2 Work out the problems using the proportions given. You may want to draw a table on rough paper to help you.

a Every box of Meltos chocolates has three milk chocolate Meltos for every four plain chocolate Meltos. A box contains 49 Meltos.

   i How many milk chocolate Meltos are in a box? _____

   ii How many plain chocolate Meltos are in a box? _____

b A bag of mixed grapes contains three green grapes for every five black grapes. A bag normally contains 48 grapes.

   i How many green grapes are there in a bag? _____

   ii How many black grapes are there? _____

Exercise 13A More multiplication

This exercise will give you practice in
- learning and using multiplication facts up to 10×10

You should know your times tables up to 10×10 already, but you can check your answers on the multiplication square.

1 Answer these either using mental methods or by using the multiplication square.

1	2	3	4	5	6	7	8	9	10
2	4	6	8	10	12	14	16	18	20
3	6	9	12	15	18	21	24	27	30
4	8	12	16	20	24	28	32	36	40
5	10	15	20	25	30	35	40	45	50
6	12	18	24	30	36	42	48	54	60
7	14	21	28	35	42	49	56	63	70
8	16	24	32	40	48	56	64	72	80
9	18	27	36	45	54	63	72	81	90
10	20	30	40	50	60	70	80	90	100

a 7×9 _____

b 9×8 _____

c 6×8 _____

d 7×4 _____

e 9×5 _____

f 7×6 _____

g 8×4 _____

h 9×3 _____

i 9×9 _____

2 Write down all the multiplication facts for each of the following numbers.

a 32 _____

b 24 _____

c 40 _____

d 54 _____

e 36 _____

3 Complete the multiplication grids.

a

×	2	4	6	8
2	4	8	12	16
3				
7				56
8		32		

b

×	3	5	7	9
6		30		
5				45
4	12			
3			21	

Exercise 13B Partitioning

This exercise will give you practice in

- partitioning techniques for adding and subtracting two-digit numbers in your head

1 Add each pair of numbers together. First add the tens and then the units. Write down your method as a calculation. The first one has been done for you.

a 47 21

40 + 20 = 60
7 + 1 = 8
60 + 8 = 68

b 57 35

c 62 32

d 76 54

e 47 34

f 56 32

g 72 41

h 88 33

i 96 21

2 Now find the difference between each pair of numbers. First subtract the tens and then the units.

a 47 – 21

b 57 – 35

c 62 – 32

d 76 – 54

e 47 – 34

f 56 – 32

g 72 – 41

h 88 – 33

i 96 – 21

3 Write five addition calculations and five subtraction calculations using the numbers below. First work them out in your head and then write down the calculations.

56   74   68   32   41   89   52   23   17   66   43   75   61

Exercise 13C Inequalities

This exercise will give you practice in

- using the symbols <, >, ?, ≤ and =

<	>	≥	≤	=
less than	greater than	greater than or equal to	less than or equal to	equal to

1 Write <, > or = between each pair of numbers to make a true statement.

a 20 _____ 21   b 31 _____ 45   c 76 _____ 76

d 86 _____ 95   e 89 _____ 98   f 23 _____ 23

g 36 _____ 54   h 21 _____ 19   i 67 _____ 78

2 Write <, > or = between each pair of numbers to make a tue statement.

a 156 _____ 166   b 178 _____ 134   c 198 _____ 230

d 144 _____ 144   e 451 _____ 667   f 656 _____ 774

g 886 _____ 886   h 155 _____ 166   i 187 _____ 234

3 Write <, > or = between each pair of numbers to make a tue statement.

a 11.43 _____ 23.54   b 16.56 _____ 16.56   c 17.89 _____ 14.32

d 21.34 _____ 36.98   e 54.32 _____ 56.51   f 87.22 _____ 93.45

g 56.16 _____ 56.16   h 65.73 _____ 88.24   i 16.42 _____ 14.62

4 Circle the numbers in the box below that are ≤ 175.

```
175        90
    180        30
   40    1      163
300      174
    70      200
```

5 Circle the numbers in the box below that are ≥ 45.

```
71        40        68
     45               44
            19
317                      30
    94      84      701
```

Exercise 13D Adjusting

This exercise will give you practice in

○ multipling by 19 or 21 by multiplying by 20 and then adjusting

 Multiply each of these numbers by 20. Write down your answers.

a 10

b 16

c 8

d 15

e 40

f 20

g 34

h 43

i 50

j 56

k 60

l 74

m 76

n 80

o 85

2 Calculate the answers to each of the following. The first one has been done for you.

a 12 × 19

$12 × 19 = (12 × 20) - 12$

$= 240 - 12$

$= 228$

b 17 × 19

c 19 × 19

d 23 × 19

e 32 × 19

f 35 × 19

g 54 × 19

h 67 × 19

3 Calculate the answers to each of the following. The first one has been done for you.

a 13×21

$13 \times 21 = (13 \times 20) + 13$

$= 260 + 13$

$= 273$

b 8×21

c 17×21

d 24×21

e 28×21

f 36×21

g 44×21

h 68×21

Exercise 13E Factor trees

This exercise will give you practice in

- finding pairs of factors of any numbers up to 100 using factor trees

1 For each set of numbers multiply one number by the other number to find the product. The first one has been done for you.

a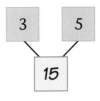

b

c

d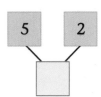

2 Write down the missing factors.

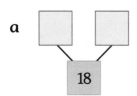 a   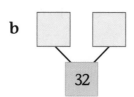 b   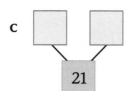 c   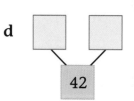 d

3 Build your own factor tree. Use the numbers below to start.

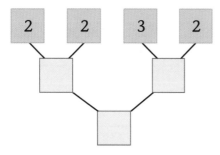 a   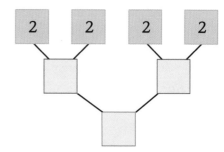 b

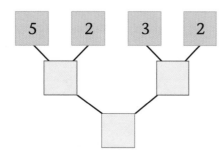 c   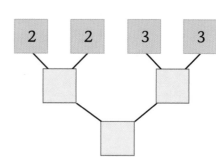 d

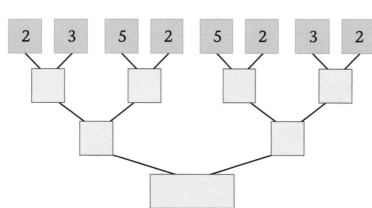 e   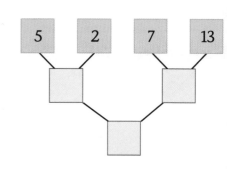 f

Exercise 14A **Symmetry**

This exercise will give you practice in
- recognising lines of symmetry in regular shapes

1 Mark any lines of symmetry with a dotted line in each of the following shapes. Don't forget to use a ruler.

a    b   c   d

2 Tick the statements which apply to a square.

a   It has two equal sides. _____

b   It has four equal sides. _____

c   It has two equal angles that are right angles. _____

d   It has two diagonals. _____

e   It has two lines of symmetry. _____

f   It has four lines of symmetry. _____

g   It has four right angles. _____

3 Complete each of the half-shapes below by reflecting them in the mirror lines marked.

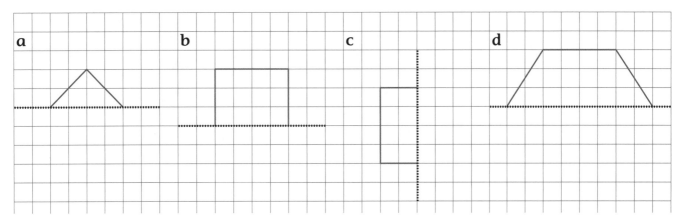

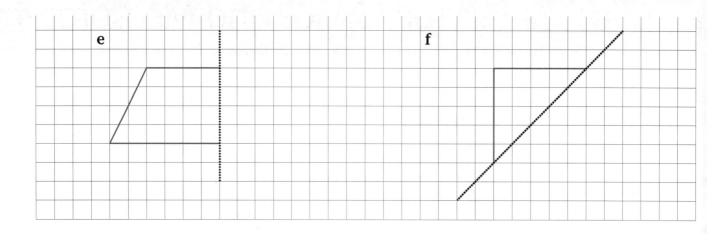

Exercise 14B Reflections

This exercise will give you practice in
- drawing reflected shapes with a mirror line

1 Reflect each of the following shapes in the mirror lines shown.

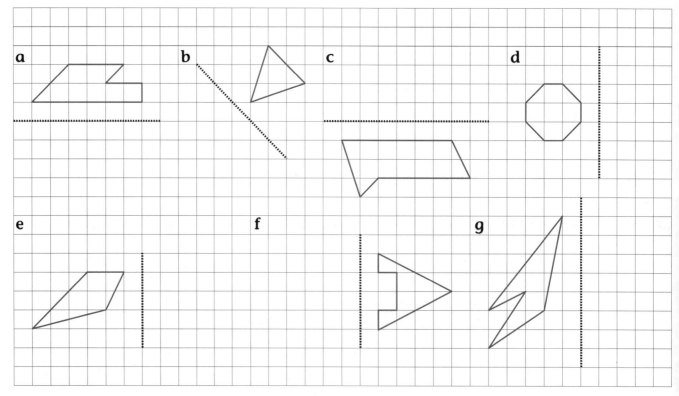

Exercise 14C **Symmetrical patterns**

This exercise will give you practice in

- completing symmetrical patterns with two lines of symmetry at right angles

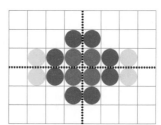

1 Check that the pattern above has two lines of symmetry. Place your mirror on the dotted lines.

2 Complete each pattern by reflecting it in both the horizontal and vertical axes of symmetry. Remember to check your reflections with a mirror.

a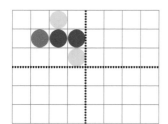

b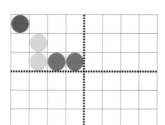

c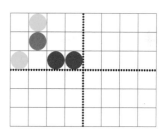

3 Complete these patterns by reflecting them across the horizontal and vertical lines of symmetry.

a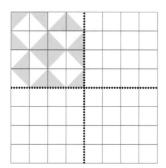

b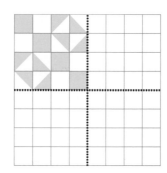

Exercise 14D Translations

This exercise will give you practice in

- recognising where a shape will be after a translation

1 **a** Write down the coordinates for shape A in the space below.

(——,——), (——,——), (——,——), (——,——)

b Write down the coordinates for shape B in the space below.

(——,——), (——,——), (——,——), (——,——)

c Complete the sentence.

Shape ——— has been translated

——— units to the right to make shape B.

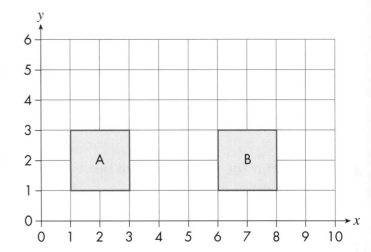

2 **a** Write down the coordinates for shape A in the space below.

(——,——), (——,——), (——,——)

b **i** Add four units to the first number in shape A's coordinates to make shape B and draw this on the grid.

   ii The coordinates for shape B are

(——,——), (——,——), (——,——).

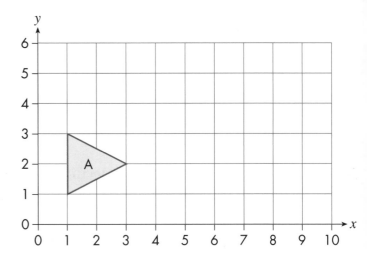

c **i** Add six units to the first number in shape A's coordinates to make shape C.

   ii The coordinates for shape C are (——,——), (——,——), (——,——).

d Complete the sentence below.

Shape ——— has been translated 6 units to make shape ———.

Exercise 14E Compass directions and turns

This exercise will give you practice in

○ understanding compass point directions

Jenny made this map of the places she visited in London.

Madame Tussauds

London Zoo

Alexandra Palace

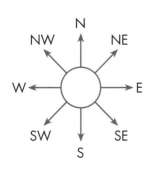

Heathrow

Buckingham Palace

St Paul's Cathedral

Westminster Abbey

Millennium Eye

Canary Wharf

1 Which building or place is:

a west of the Millennium Eye? _____

b north of Buckingham Palace? _____

c south of St Paul's Cathedral? _____

2 You are at Buckingham Palace, which building or place is:

a to the north-east? _____

b to the south-west? _____

3 You are still at Buckingham Palace. Face Heathrow Airport. Turn clockwise through 90°. Which direction are you facing? What can you see?

_____

4 You are on the Millennium Eye. Face Buckingham Palace. Turn to face the north-east. What can you see?

_____

Exercise 15A From bar-line charts to line graphs

This exercise will give you practice in

- drawing a temperature–time bar-line graph and using it to solve problems

During his summer holidays, Jack recorded the temperatures in his garden on 22nd August. The results are shown in the table on the right.

Time	Temperature (°C)
7:30 am	12
8:30 am	14
9:30 am	16
10:30 am	16
11:30 am	20
12:30 pm	22

1 What was the temperature at 9:30 am? _____

2 When was the temperature 20°C? _____

3 Draw a bar-line chart for the data on the axes below.

4 Join up the tops of the bars on your graph using a ruler.

5 What was the temperature at 11:00 am?

_____

6 Between what times was the temperature the same?

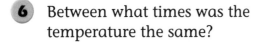

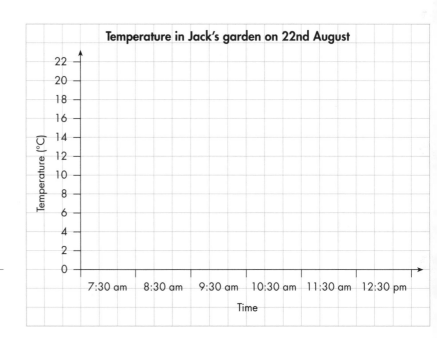

_____

Exercise 15B Line graphs

This exercise will give you practice in

- reading data represented in a temperature–time line graph

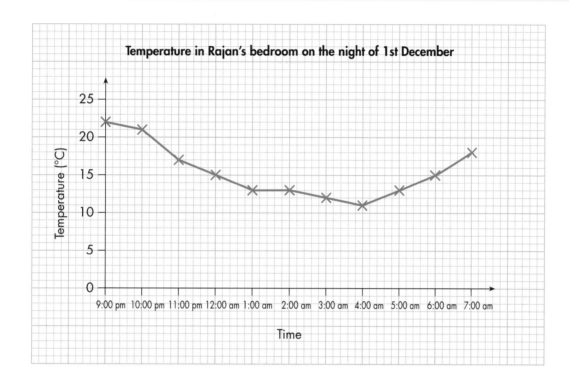

Temperature in Rajan's bedroom on the night of 1st December

The graph shows the temperature in Rajan's bedroom one night.

1 What was the temperature at 11.00 pm? _____

2 When was the temperature 21°C? _____

3 When was it hottest? _____

4 What was the coldest temperature? _____

5 Between what times did the temperature stay the same? _____

6 After what time did the temperature start to rise? _____

7 Complete the table by reading the data from the graph.

Time	Temperature (°C)
9:00 pm	22
10:00 pm	21
11:00 pm	17
12:00 am	15
1:00 am	13
2:00 am	13
3:00 am	
4:00 am	
5:00 am	
6:00 am	
7:00 am	

Exercise 15C Bar-line charts

This exercise will give you practice in

- solving problems by drawing and reading data from a bar-line chart

1 Roll a die 40 times. Record the numbers you throw in the tally chart.

Number	Tally	Frequency
1		
2		
3		
4		
5		
6		

2 Write down the frequencies for each number in the table.

3 Complete the bar-line chart

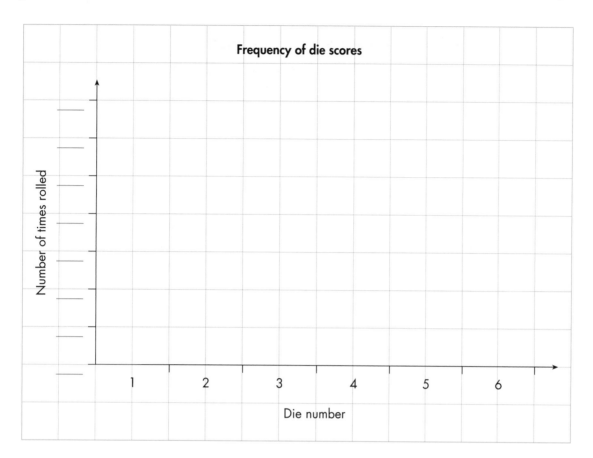

Frequency of die scores

Number of times rolled

Die number

4 Which number did you roll the most? _____

5 What is this number called? _____

6 How many times did you roll a four? _____

7 Which number did you roll least? _____

Exercise 15D Distance-time graphs

This exercise will give you practice in

- solving problems by reading results from a distance–time graph

Alice delivers post in her van. The line graph shows her journey.

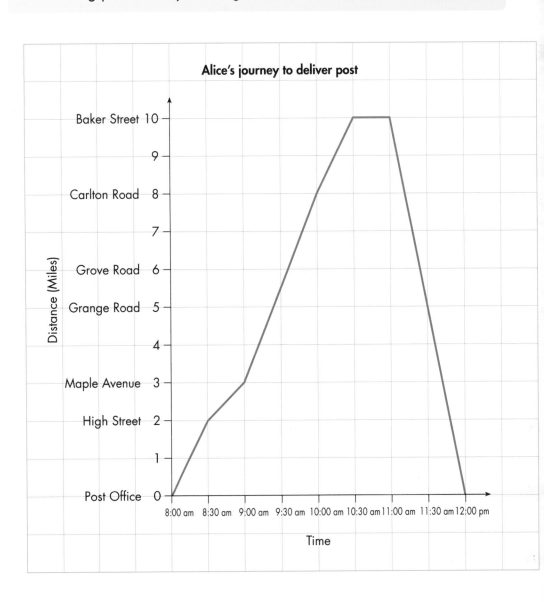

Alice's journey to deliver post

1. Where did Alice deliver post first? What time did she get there?

_____

2. Where was her next stop? How far is it from the post office?

_____

3. What do you think was happening between 10:30 and 11:00?

_____

4 What time did Alice start her return journey to the post office? _____

5 How far is Carlton Road from the post office? _____

6 What time did Alice get back to the post office? _____

Exercise 15E More line graphs

This exercise will give you practice in

- solving problems by drawing and reading data from a line graph

Surround Sounds are having a CD sale. The owner has placed this poster in the window of the shop.

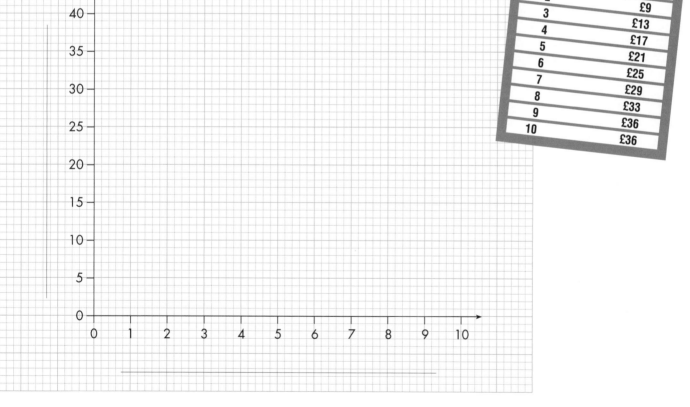

Number of CDs Bought	Price
1	£5
2	£9
3	£13
4	£17
5	£21
6	£25
7	£29
8	£33
9	£36
10	£36

1 Label the axes on the graph and give the graph a title.

2 How much do 0 CDs cost? _____ Plot this point on the graph.

3 How much does one CD cost? _____ Plot this point on the graph.

4 Continue plotting the points on the graph.

5 Join up your points.

6 How much do eight CDs cost? _____

7 Do you think that buying two CDs instead of one CD is value for money? Explain your answer.

_____

_____

8 Why do you think that the price for nine CDs is the same as for 10 CDs.

_____

_____

Exercise 16A Place value in mental addition

This exercise will give you practice in

- using known facts and place value to help with mental addition techniques

1 Write down the answers to each of these calculations.

a 6 + 4 + 3 _____

    60 + 40 + 30 _____

    600 + 400 + 300 _____

b 6 + 2 + 1 _____

    60 + 20 + 10 _____

    600 + 200 + 100 _____

c 8 + 5 + 2 _____

    80 + 50 + 20 _____

    800 + 500 + 200 _____

d 140 + 150 _____

e 220 + 260 _____

f 340 + 150 _____

g 120 + 230 _____

h 160 + 280 _____

i 330 + 450 _____

2 Work out the first calculation and use it to help you work out the other two.

a 2 + 5 + 8 + 3 _____

    20 + 50 + 80 + 30 _____

    200 + 500 + 800 + 300 _____

b 6 + 7 + 2 + 4 _____

    60 + 70 + 20 + 40 _____

    600 + 700 + 200 + 400 _____

c 600 + 400 + 700 + 300 _____

    60 + 40 + 70 + 30 _____

    6 + 4 + 7 + 3 _____

d 80 + 10 + 90 + 50 _____

    8 + 1 + 9 + 5 _____

    800 + 100 + 900 + 500 _____

e 700 + 800 + 400 + 500 + 200 _____

    70 + 80 + 40 + 50 + 20 _____

    7 + 8 + 4 + 5 + 2 _____

Exercise 16B Adding decimals

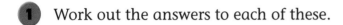

This exercise will give you practice in
- adding pairs of decimal fractions

1 Work out the answers to each of these.

   a £16.43 + £12.56   **b** £12.67 + £11.99   **c** £14.56 + £19.60

   d £22.64 + £26.89   **e** £24.99 + £29.99   **f** £34.56 + £44.21

2 Calculate each of the following.

   a 4.5 m + 3.85 m   **b** 5.65 m + 4.78 m   **c** 9.7 m + 6.2 m

   d 9.65 m + 3.92 m   **e** 12.3 m + 13.6 m   **f** 18.65 m + 14.72 m

3 Work out the answers to each of these.

a   9.65 kg + 3.67 kg

b   10.73 kg + 11.98 kg

c   21.33 kg + 66.73 kg

d   78.45 kg + 82.34 kg

e   79.65 kg + 89.54 kg

f   88.56 kg + 44.76 kg

Exercise 16C Subtracting decimals

This exercise will give you practice in

- subtracting pairs of decimal fractions

1 Work out the answers to each of these.

a   £46.12 – £37.08

b   £37.43 – £28.27

c   £56.43 – £31.85

d   £86.42 – £36.56

e   £88.42 – £63.45

f   £93.45 – £52.56

2 Calculate each of the following.

    a 8.63 m – 4.35 m   **b** 14.3 cm – 9.6 cm   **c** 17.83 m – 14.62 m

    d 18.6 km – 15.9 km   **e** 24.45 m – 19.34 m   **f** 34.62 km – 23.95 km

3 Work out the answers to each of the following.

    a 23.4 kg – 12.6 kg   **b** 19.58 kg – 11.01 kg   **c** 33.25 kg – 29.88 kg

    d 78.21 kg – 70.56 kg   **e** 90.84 kg – 87.65 kg   **f** 33.3 kg – 29.9 kg

Exercise 16D Multiplying decimals

This exercise will give you practice in

- estimating
- multiplying decimals

1 Partition each of these numbers into whole numbers and decimal numbers.
The first one has been done for you.

a 4.3 _= 4.0 + 0.3_   **b** 2.4 _____   **c** 5.6 _____

d 6.5 _____   **e** 7.5 _____   **f** 7.7 _____

g 8.2 _____   **h** 1.8 _____   **i** 9.5 _____

j 2.9 _____   **k** 3.6 _____   **l** 9.9 _____

2 Work out the answer to each of these decimal multiplications following the steps below.

    1 write down an estimate

    2 work out the calculation by partitioning the whole numbers from the decimal numbers

The first one has been done for you.

a 4.3×4

    Estimate: $4 \times 4 = 16$

            $4.0 \times 4 = 16$

            $0.3 \times 4 = 1.2$

                   $= 17.2$

b 7.8×4

c 6.5×4

d 4.6×5

e 5.6×4

f 9.9×5

g 5.8×4

h 6.2×5

i 6.3×4

j 4.9×6

Exercise 16E Problem solving

This exercise will give you practice in

- using addition, subtraction, multiplication and division to solve real-life problems involving money

Work out each of the following problems. Explain briefly the method you used to solve the problem.

1 One Saturday I went out with £24.50 and came home with £1.52. I bought a CD for £11.99 and spent the rest on a T-shirt. How much was the T-shirt?

2 The school raised £145.60 during its charity day. £34.80 was made on the cake stall and £56.80 was made from the Year 7 non-uniform day. The rest was made from a sponsored silence by the teachers. How much did the sponsored silence make?

3 The ICT Department has just spent £1453 on new equipment for the ICT suite. £200 was spent on new keyboards. The rest of the money was spent evenly between new printers and new scanners. How much was spent on printers?

4 I was given £85 for Christmas. I bought two CDs which were £11.99 each and a pair of jeans that cost £39. I bought my brother a book and came home with £17.03. How much was the book for my brother?

Exercise 17A   Polygons

This exercise will give you practice in

○ classifying 2-D shapes according to regularity, symmetry and angles

1 Look at the shapes below. Decide whether each shape is regular or irregular and write the letter of each shape in the correct box.

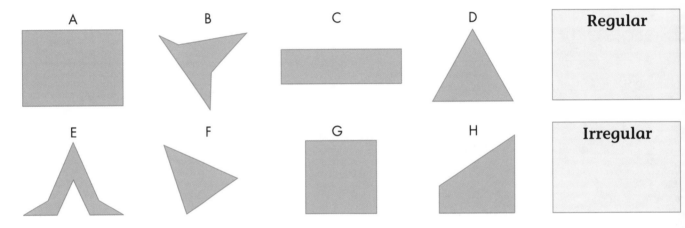

Regular	
Irregular	

2 Look at the shapes below. Decide whether each contains at least 1 right angle or not. Write the letter of each shape in the correct box.

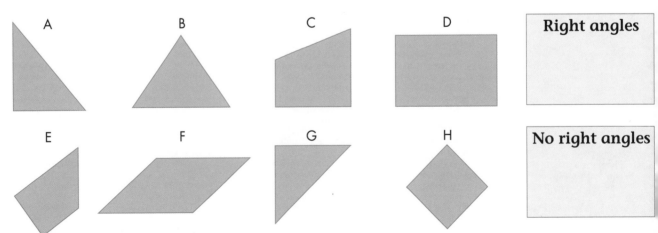

Right angles	
No right angles	

3 Look at the shapes below. Decide whether each has either no lines of symmetry or one or more lines of symmetry. Write the letter of each shape in the correct box.

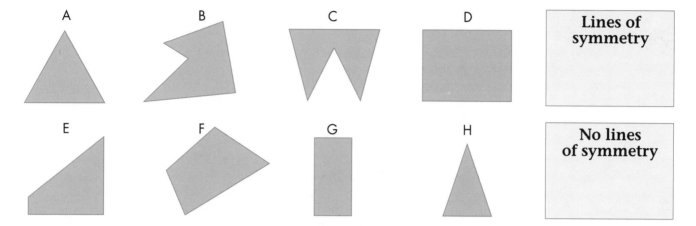

Exercise 17B Tessellations

This exercise will give you practice in
- recognising and extending patterns of shapes

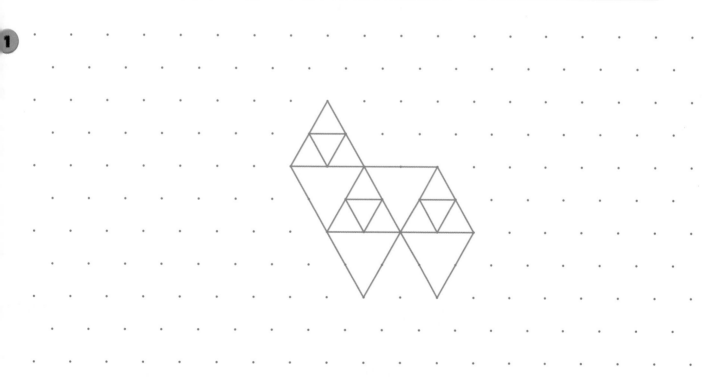

a Continue the pattern until you cannot fit any more triangles on the page.

b Colour your pattern so that triangles next to each other do not have the same colour. Use the least number of colours possible.

2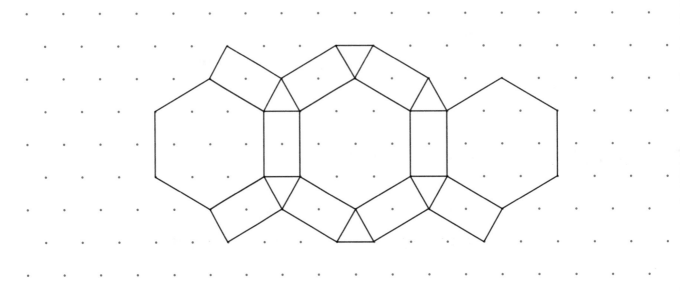

a   Name all of the shapes used to make this pattern. _____

_____

b   Continue the pattern until you cannot fit any more shapes on the page.

c   Colour your pattern so that shapes next to each other do not have the same colour. Use the least number of colours possible.

Exercise 17C 3-D shapes

This exercise will give you practice in

- classifying 3-D shapes

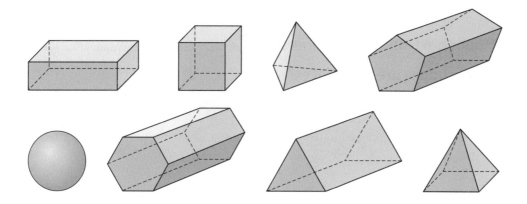

1 Complete the table below by classifying the 3-D shapes above.

Shape	Number of faces	Number of vertices	Is it a polyhedron	Is it a prism?
Cube	6	8	Yes	Yes

2 **a** Which shape is not a prism or a polyhedron? _____

    b Why is this? _____

_____

3 Which of the 3-D shapes have at least one square face? _____

_____

4 Which of the 3-D shapes have at least one triangular face? _____

_____

5 Which shape appears in the answer to both **Questions 3** and **4**?

_____

6 **a** Which shapes have all identical faces? _____

b What type of shapes are these faces? _____

Published by HarperCollins*Publishers* Limited
77–85 Fulham Palace Road
Hammersmith
London
W6 8JB

Browse the complete Collins catalogue at
www.collinseducation.com

© HarperCollins*Publishers* Ltd 2004

10 9 8 7 6 5 4 3

ISBN 0 00 717019 X

British Library Cataloguing in Publication Data
A Catalogue record for this publication is available from the
British Library

Design and typesetting by Jordan Publishing Design
Covers by Chi Leung
Illustrations by Nigel Jordan and Tony Wilkins
Production by Sarah Robinson
Printed and bound by Martins the Printers Ltd, Berwick upon Tweed

The publishers would like to thank the many teachers and
advisers whose feedback helped to shape *Maths
Frameworking*.

You might also like to visit
www.harpercollins.co.uk
The book lover's website